SONGS AND STORIES
ABOUT
ANIMALS

BY

ETHEL CROWNINSHIELD

THE BOSTON MUSIC COMPANY   BOSTON, MASS.

Acknowledgement is due to Ginn & Company for permission to use the poems: "The Kangaroo" from SING A SONG and "Little Turtle" from LISTEN AND SING of *The World of Music*, copyright 1936.

FOREWORD

The wise parent or teacher should look for and find in any gift for a child, a means of entertainment and a medium of education. So much progress has been made in gift material that this is not difficult to do.

STORIES AND SONGS ABOUT ANIMALS has many uses. First of all, it is fun. The stories may be dramatized. The words of the songs can and should be used as poems. They are also a direct aid towards dramatization. The music is rhythmic. The sentences short and the stories easily re-told by the child.

This book lends itself to a reading-readiness program and will be found most helpful in correcting speech defects.

The interest aroused by the combination of words, dramatization and song will encourage self-expression, giving poise and overcoming self-consciousness.

The pictures in this book were drawn by children between five and six years of age. They will prove stimulating to the imagination and perhaps create a desire in other children to draw pictures for themselves.

E. C.

TABLE OF CONTENTS

Listen to a story,

Listen to a song.

All of them are lots of fun,

None of them are long.

PETER PETER PENGUIN

Peter Peter was a penguin who lived near the South Pole. There were many other penguins who lived there, but Peter was the nicest of them all. Do you know why?

Peter had lots of brothers and sisters. He had lots of friends too. He liked every one of them. Each day he would make up a new game for them to play. Sometimes they would play swimming tag. Sometimes they would jump off the high hills of ice into the water. Sometimes they would have a parade. This was the game they liked best of all.

Peter Peter would lead them. When the penguins marched by, all the Mother and Father penguins would sing a penguin song to them. All the little penguins would sing too and march home to have their supper and go to bed.

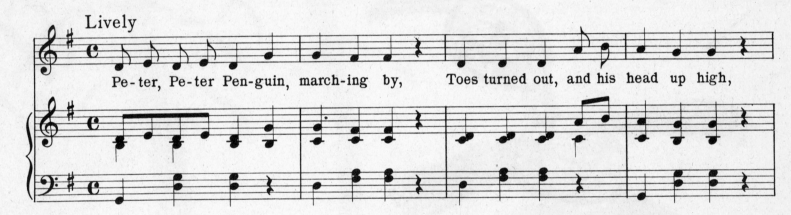

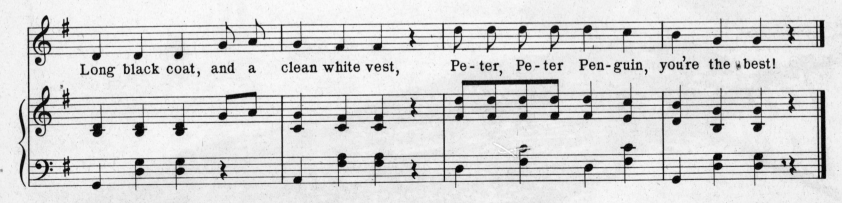

B.M.Co. 10823

THE BIG CROCODILE

Once there was a crocodile.   He was a great big crocodile.   His mouth was so big, it looked like a deep, dark cave. He had so many teeth, you couldn't count them.   He lived in a swamp, in the woods.

Close by, on the edge of the woods, was a little house.   In the house lived a boy who looked just like Little Black Sambo.   Every morning, he would walk down into the swamp and call,

"Crocodile, crocodile, lying in the sun,
Crocodile, crocodile, you can't run!"

The crocodile would open his big mouth and slash his long tail around.   That was all he did, because he really couldn't run very fast.   His legs were too short.

The little boy was too smart to go close to him.   After a while the little boy would run home again, calling,

"Crocodile, crocodile, one, two, three,
Crocodile, crocodile, can't catch me!"

The crocodile never did catch the little boy.   He didn't want to run.   He thought it was much more fun, to lie quietly in the sun.

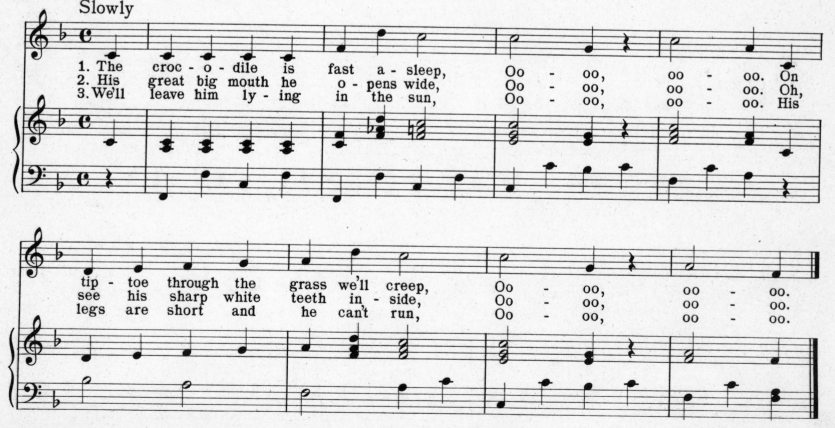

SAMMY SEA GULL

Sammy Sea Gull did not know his name was Sammy. Only Mary Lou knew it because she had given him his name. Every day Sammy Sea Gull would stand on one foot, on a high post, at the end of the wharf. He stood so still that he looked as if he were made out of wood. The wind could not blow him off although it tried very hard.

When Sammy was tired of standing on one foot, he would spread his wings and fly away over the blue water. Mary Lou watched him. One day she put on her bathing suit and climbed up on the post. It seemed very high. She could not stand as still on two feet, as Sammy had stood on one. When she spread out her arms and tried to fly, she fell splash into the water.

The water was not very deep so she waded out safe and sound. Mary Lou said,

"I can walk, I can run,
I can swim if I try.
Unless I get an airplane
I can never, never fly!"

Sea gull fly-ing o-ver the wa-ter, Fly-ing high in the sky so blue,

Sea gull fly-ing o-ver the wa-ter, I wish that I were a sea gull too!

B.M.Co. 10823

THE WHALE

Hardly any one ever sees a whale. The whale lives in the ocean and you would have to sail far away to find one.
If you have ever seen a book about Pinocchio, then you have seen a picture of a whale. There was a big whale in that story. It was a magic whale because it could do very strange things. Maybe some day you can sail far away and see a real whale. That will not be magic, but just your good luck.
I am sure you would not be like the boy, who thought he could catch a whale in his mother's pail. Even if you caught one in the ocean, it would be so big, you would not know what to do with it. That is why it is more fun to see a whale than to catch one.

Do you think you'll ev-er see a whale, Long and black with a big strong tail,
Just like a boat with-out a sail? Do you think you'll ev-er see a whale?

B.M.Co. 10823

SIMON THE SEAL

Simon was a little black seal. Once he had lived way up north. He and his brothers and sisters were very good swimmers. One day they all took a long swim and Simon found himself on a beach, far away from home.

He was sitting on a big rock, when along came a man. All the other seals jumped into the water and swam away. Simon sat quite still. The man came close to him and picked him up. Simon knew the man was his friend. The man carried Simon home with him. He fed him. He played with him. He taught him to do tricks. Simon liked to do tricks.

He could bounce a ball with his nose. He could roll over. He could catch a fish when the man tossed it to him. When all the people clapped their hands, Simon would clap loudest of all with his two front paws. Wasn't he a smart little seal?

Oh, Si - mon is a lit - tle black seal As smart as he can be, He can bounce a ball and ring a bell, And count way up to three.

B.M. Co. 10823

THE MONKEY

Once there was a man who had a hand organ and a monkey. In the summertime you could hear his music. At first it sounded far away, then it came nearer and nearer. Soon you could see the organ-man and his monkey coming around the corner.

The children would stand in a circle about the monkey. They gave him their pennies instead of spending them for candy.

At Christmas time a funny thing happened. When the children went in town to see Santa Claus, in the big store, what do you think they found? Why, their friend, the monkey! He was still taking pennies in his cap.

They gave the monkey a few pennies because it was fun. The rest of their pennies they kept to buy Christmas presents for their friends.

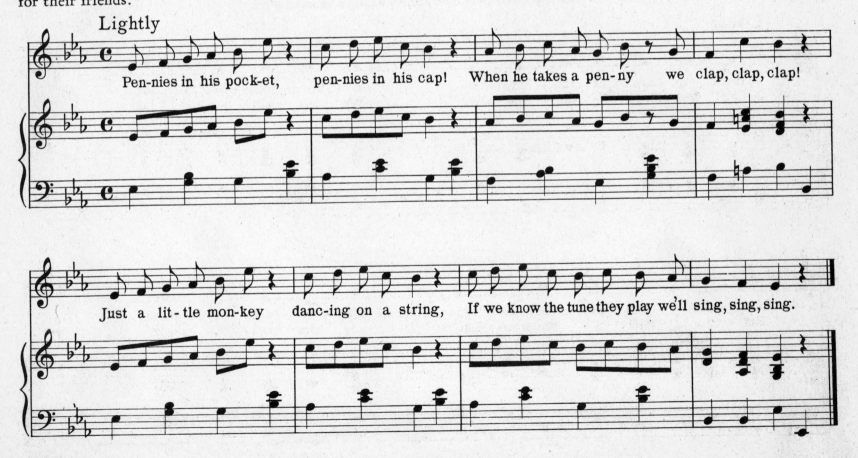

Pen-nies in his pock-et, pen-nies in his cap! When he takes a pen-ny we clap, clap, clap!

Just a lit-tle mon-key danc-ing on a string, If we know the tune they play we'll sing, sing, sing.

B.M.Co. 10823

THE BIG GIRAFFE

The circus was in town.   Connie and John were going with their Father.   They had talked about it for days and knew there would be lots to see.   They wanted to start early.   They did not want to miss anything.

When they came to the circus grounds, there were two big tents.   They bought their tickets and went inside.   All the animals were in the first tent.   There were hundreds of people there and it was hard to get close to the cages.   Connie and John could see the elephants because they were big.   They could hear the lions and tigers roaring.   There were so many people around the monkeys' cage that they could hardly see the monkeys at all.

There was one animal that everybody could see.   He had long legs and a long neck.   No matter where you stood, you could see him.   It was the big giraffe.   Connie and John liked him best of all.

When they went inside the big circus tent, they had seats where they could see everything.   They saw the clowns, the horses and all the animals that came in to do tricks.   When they went home, it was the giraffe that they remembered best of all.   Connie said, it was because he looked over everyone's head, just at them.

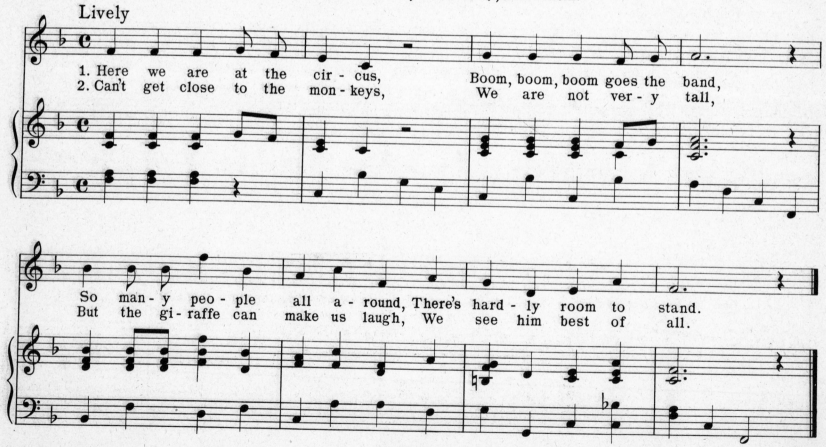

1. Here we are at the cir - cus, Boom, boom, boom goes the band,
2. Can't get close to the mon - keys, We are not ver - y tall,

So man - y peo - ple all a - round, There's hard - ly room to stand.
But the gi - raffe can make us laugh, We see him best of all.

B.M.Co. 10823

THE KANGAROO

Father has pockets in his trousers. Mother has pockets in her jacket. You have pockets in your coat. Father carries money in his pockets. Mother carries money in hers, sometimes. You carry a clean handkerchief in yours.

Does your dog have a pocket? Does your cat have a pocket? No! Neither does a rabbit, nor a cow, nor a pony!

There is an animal though who does have a pocket. It is a kangaroo. What do you think she carries in her pocket? Her baby! Are you surprised?

Far a-way lived a kan-ga-roo Who ate so much that he grew and grew, When he was lit-tle he hopped to bed, But now he gives a big leap in-stead.

B.M. Co. 10823

THE POLAR BEAR

Once there was a polar bear who lived way up north, where the snow was very deep.   He had to crack the ice when he wanted to go in swimming.   He did not think it was too cold.   He had a thick fur coat and, best of all, it was white.   When he went for a walk or went to find his breakfast, it was hard to see him.   He looked just like the snow.   No one could ever catch him.   He grew and grew to be the biggest polar bear in the north.

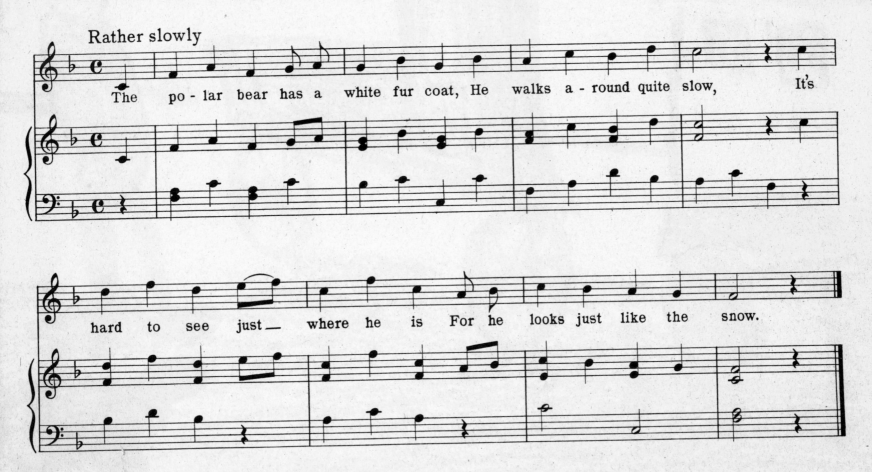

MR. TURTLE

Mr. Gilhooly had an automobile. There was a trailer hitched to the back of it. The trailer was a little house. Everywhere Mr. Gilhooly went, his house went too. Every time Mr. Gilhooly stopped, his house stopped too. When it rained, it kept Mr. Gilhooly dry. When it was cold, it kept Mr. Gilhooly warm. When it was hot; it kept Mr. Gilhooly cool.

One day as he was driving along, he saw something in the road moving very slowly. Mr. Gilhooly stopped his automobile and his house stopped too, of course. Mr. Gilhooly got out and there, in front of him, what do you think he saw? A turtle, a big turtle! Mr. Turtle carried his house on his back, instead of behind him. "Well," said Mr. Gilhooly, "here is a friend of mine, to be sure! He carries his house along with him too!" He picked Mr. Turtle up and Mr. Gilhooly and his house and Mr. Turtle and his house rode away together.

Evenly

1. Lit-tle tur-tle, lit-tle tur-tle, For a house he'll nev-er lack, Far a-
2. When the sun's no long-er shin-ing, When the rain-drops gen-tly fall, He's no

way though he may trav-el, Tur-tle's house is on his back.
need for an um-brel-la, He will not get wet at all.

POLLY PARROT

Mary had a parrot that did not have to live in a cage. It could stand on a perch, in the living room and take care of itself. The parrot's name was Polly. She could talk almost as well as Mary. Her feathers were green and red.

Mary had a doll, but whom do you think she liked to take out in the doll carriage? Why, Polly Parrot! Polly would let Mary dress her up in the doll's clothes. When Mary covered her up with a blanket, Polly would lie quite still. She would not keep too still though, she would call,

"Hello, hello, here we go!
Hello, hello, here we go!"

How surprised everyone was who passed! Mary's friends had dolls who could say, "Mamma," and some of the dolls could cry. No one had a doll who could talk. Mary was very proud of Polly Parrot and thought she was almost as good as a baby brother.

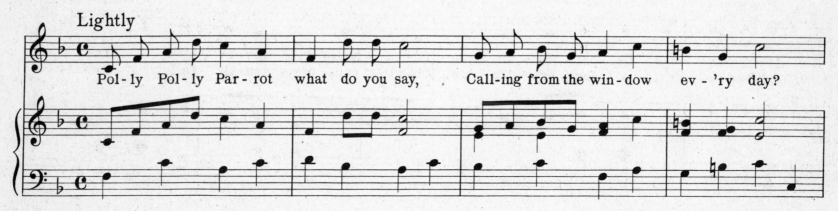

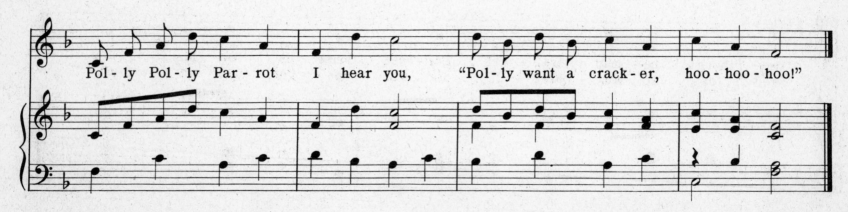

B.M.Co. 10823

MR. TOAD

Once there was a toad who lived in a garden. It was a beautiful garden! It had tall flowers and short flowers, red flowers and yellow flowers, blue flowers and white flowers. Every day the butterflies and bees would fly over the garden. Every night the fireflies would fly over and flash their lights, just like a fairy's airplane.

The toad was not beautiful. He was quite ugly to look at. He couldn't fly, he could only hop, but he knew how to take care of a garden. He ate up all the little bugs that hurt the flowers. He could hop everywhere, close to the ground and take care of every single flower.

One day a little girl came into the garden. The toad was right in the middle of the path. The little girl was skipping along and did not see Mr. Toad until she was very close to him. The toad did not have time to hop away, so he just sat there blinking his eyes. The little girl knew all about toads. She knew how they helped take care of gardens. She stood in front of him and said, "Thank you, Mr. Toad," and sang a song to him.

Mr. Toad sat very still and listened to the song, then he hopped away. The little girl kept on singing and picked a big bunch of flowers for her Mother's birthday.

BLACK CAT

Billy was a black cat who lived in an alley. He had lots of friends. The laundry man gave him his breakfast. The cook, in the restaurant, gave him his dinner. The grocery man gave him his supper.

In between, he would sit on back door steps and "meau!" Someone always came out and said, "Poor kitty, he is hungry!" They would put out some milk or some scraps and Billy would eat another dinner. You see, he was a very fat and lucky cat!

It was Halloween and the grocery man wanted his window to look nice. He had pumpkins, jack-o-lanterns and an old lady-witch in it, but he did not have a black cat. The grocery man wanted a black cat. That night when he gave Billy his supper, he put the saucer just inside the door. Billy walked in. When he had finished eating, he tried to walk out, but the door was shut.

Just then the grocery man picked Billy up and put him in the window along with the pumpkins, the jack-o-lanterns and the old lady-witch. He put out the lights, locked up the store and went home.

That night, everybody who passed the grocery store, could see all the Halloween things in the window. Best of all, they saw a real black cat, blinking his green eyes at the old lady-witch. All the children who stopped to look in the window said that the old lady-witch was blinking her green eyes too.

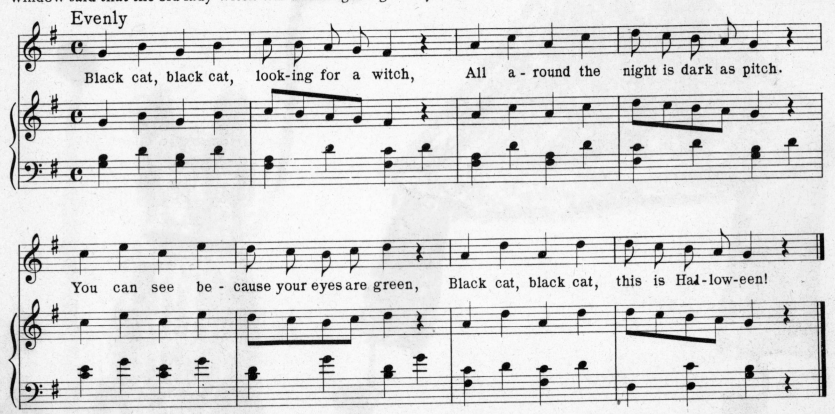

Black cat, black cat, look-ing for a witch, All a-round the night is dark as pitch.
You can see be-cause your eyes are green, Black cat, black cat, this is Hal-low-een!

B.M.Co. 10823

MY DOG

Yu San was a little Chinese girl. She could not understand all the things that were said to her because, at home, her mother and father spoke only Chinese words. Every day she learned a few new words in school and she could always smile.

Yu San had a dog who came to school with her every day. The dog could smile too, he wagged his tail every time anyone spoke to him. One day Yu San came to school dressed in a real Chinese dress. It was her birthday and even her dog had a birthday present. It was a new red collar. Yu San looked so pretty, the children drew pictures of her. One of them is in this book.

Yu San liked the pictures and took one of them home. She said, "It is for my Mother. I say to her every day, 'I love you!' My dog can say, 'I love you,' too, but he says it with his eyes."

So Yu San went home smiling, with her picture, her dog, and her happy heart.

Peo - ple al - ways talk with words, But my dog is wise.

He can say, "I love you," But he says it with his eyes.

B.M.Co. 10823